SHAGGY SH

Tracey Elliot-Ree

TRACEY ELLIOT-REEP

© Tracey Elliot-Reep 2013
© Photographs and sketches by Tracey Elliot-Reep
Shilstone Rocks
Widecombe-in-the-Moor
Dartmoor TQ13 7TF
England

ISBN 978-0-9538231-9-2

Jacob Girl

Start

Tracey with Blue and Topnotch.
And her favourites in sketches

Blue and Zeeba

Jacob

In memory of
Badger, Blue, Babe, Sooty, Diamond, Start and all my sheep

All creatures great and small the Lord God made them all.
And what a variety!

Oh, to be in England
Now that April's there
— Robert Browning

It's the Dartmoor Derby! Dartmoor Whiteface lambs.

7

HISTORY

Sheep have grazed in Great Britain, providing wool and food, for thousands of years. Britain has more than 60 pedigree breeds, not including crossbreeds – many more than any other country in the world.

Sheep spread from Asia to Africa, and to Europe. In fact, ancestors of the Jacob sheep are mentioned in Genesis, the very first book of the Bible. The Romans became skilled sheep breeders and one of their citizens, living in Spain, developed the foundation stock of a breed we know today as the Merino.

Before the Roman invasion of Britain in 55 BC, this country kept small sheep like the Soay, and spun and weaved using their wool. The Romans then introduced a larger breed with white wool, and left these sheep behind when they departed. The next invaders, the Vikings, brought a black-faced, horned sheep – ancestors of the Blackface, Swaledale and Herdwick. From this mix, various breeds evolved in the lowlands, hills and highlands of Britain.

In 1808, 14,000 Dartmoor Whiteface sheep were accounted for in Widecombe parish alone and 110,000 were summer pastured on Dartmoor.

Whitefaced Dartmoor, Barramoor Farm

Herdwick

Ryeland Lamb

Sheep and their wool were making this country prosperous in the 12th century. Wool was being exported, and the largest flocks were bred by the landowning abbeys and monasteries. By the 15th century, England was largely a nation of sheep farmers and cloth manufacturers.

The Ryeland is typical of the fine, short-wooled sheep kept in Britain during the middle ages, and the Romney is probably similar to the medieval long-wooled breed.

The quality of the wool was the main criteria for breeding until the 18th century and it wasn't until the industrial revolution that meat became the main priority – it was needed to feed the growing industrial areas.

Soay

Romney

Dartmoor Greyface ewe and lamb at Barramoor Farm.

RARE BREEDS

The fascinating variety of native British breeds fall into four major categories: Primitive, Longwool, Hill and Down Breed sheep. The Primitive breeds originate in remote islands, have not been crossbred and have developed unique characteristics which mean they are tough and can survive where larger, more 'developed' sheep would not. Their fleeces are often attractively coloured and are popular with smallholders and handspinners. Some of these Primitive breeds moult their fleeces or can be plucked, which means they don't need to be shorn. Although tiny in comparison with some larger breeds, some of these little characters can make up for their size by growing two, four or even six horns!

The North Ronaldsay, an endangered rare breed, is still found on its native island – the northernmost of the Orkneys. A stone wall was built on the island in 1832 to keep the sheep on the seashore, away from the cultivated land. Since then, the sheep have primarily survived on seaweed.

Manx Loaghtan: The word Loaghtan is Manx for 'mouse brown', and although the lambs are born black, they quickly lighten in colour. They have grazed the slopes of the Isle of Man for hundreds of years.

Dartmoor Whiteface are a rare breed.

Hill Sheep are hardy and capable of surviving in the harsh uplands of Britain. They are often crossed with Down breeds and produce 'Mule' sheep, combining the toughness of the hills with the fast-growing characteristics of the lowlands. The Badger Face Welsh Mountain is thought to be one of the oldest British breeds, with origins tracing back to the 1st century.

The Longwool breeds were developed for their fleeces and some of them produce up to 20kg of wool, often with lustrous ringlets. Left: The Lincoln Longwool is the largest British breed, producing the heaviest, longest and most lustrous fleece of any worldwide. It is an 'At Risk' rare breed.

Down breeds, from the lowlands, are docile sheep and produce big, quick-growing lambs for meat.
Dorset Down was produced in the late 1800s by crossing downland Berkshire, Hampshire and Wiltshire ewes with Southdown rams. These 'improved' sheep were introduced to downland flocks in Dorset, where they thrived.

15

Poll Dorset

This Southdown ewe's lamb had died and its coat was put on an orphan lamb.
The ewe accepted the orphan because it smelt like her own lamb.

> Logic will get you from A to B. Imagination will take you everywhere
> - Albert Einstein

A magazine commissioned me to photograph a Southdown flock in Wiltshire. I knew I'd need a special, atmospheric light to make an interesting picture. I imagined dawn would be best, so I left Dartmoor at 3am in a borrowed pick-up and drove three and a half hours to Wiltshire. My prayer was answered: as the sun rose, it illuminated the landscape, causing the frosted sheep and grass to sparkle.

Badger with Babe, Sooty and Blue.

Early shepherding times

My sheep hear my voice. I know them by name and they follow me - Jesus

I began looking after a small, mixed breed flock after Badger (one of my mother's old ewes) had triplets, but didn't have enough milk to go around. I called these lambs Sooty, Babe and Blue (the last one got her name because I had to put a blue spot on the back of her head just to tell her apart from Babe!).

I took a lambing course and, in the years that followed, my sleep during the spring would often be interrupted by night-time trips to check up on the ewes and lambs. I didn't do it for wages or profit – simply because I cared for my sheep… and they knew it! Even when I was a long way off and they heard my voice they would bleat to me. I knew them each by name, and I loved them.

All three of the triplets grew up to have their own lambs, and I'd organise my international travels just to be on standby during the lambing season. Blue liked me to be near at hand and, once she gave birth, she'd lick her lambs and then lick me – proudly sharing her twins with me (who were usually large). I called two of them Zeeba and Buzzbe.

"Look Mum I can fly!" Zeeba launches off - as a carefree lamb!

I would have been glad to have lived under my wood side, and to have kept a flock of sheep, rather than to have undertaken this government. – Oliver Cromwell

My little flock of sheep and some other little friends!

Mum (Blue), you have to get up as I want some milk!

Midnight Crisis

Late one night, after checking the maternity ward in the barn, I was heading for bed when I felt an urge to check on the ewes in the field. I hesitated, telling myself that they weren't ready to lamb, and wearily turned again for my bed.

However, just for peace of mind I headed back and shone my torch over the field. That was when I noticed a lamb's head poking out of a ewe's hind end. It was swollen, with no sign of the correctly presented forelegs. This young ewe was the biggest and wildest, and also a first time lamber. There was no one around to help me, so I breathed out, "help me God!"

Playtime!

First I had to catch her. I washed under the farm tap and greased my right arm up to my elbow. With the torch slung around my neck, I tried to catch her with my left hand, to keep my right hand clean, but she was too strong. I stalked her around the dark field and pounced when she lay down, once again trying to birth the lamb.

Feeling like an octopus, using my body to pin her to the ground, I carefully pushed the lamb's head back and felt for the lamb's forelegs inside her womb. I found one, then two, and cupped the little hooves in my palm (so they wouldn't rip her womb). I then brought them to front and gently pulled the lamb out – at which point the ewe ran off into the darkness!

"Now what?" I sighed. Hoping she'd return, I laid the lamb in the grass and backed off, illuminating it with the beam of light. At last, curiosity attracted the ewe and she returned to lick her first born.

Spring is a new beginning.
It's a season of young life, of lambs and spring buds
Yellow is its colour. The warm yellow of the sun,
of the bright dandelion and the daffodil.

Blackface

The Scotch Blackface, a tough, high country sheep of Scotland and other highlands, is thought to date back to the 12th century, when the monks used its wool for clothing and for exporting to Europe.

Swaledale

Scotland

29

Eyes to see and ears to hear, both are gifts from God - Proverb

This is Snowdrop (above), who I helped into the world, who grew into a big Texel sheep. She produced many big lambs herself, but on one occasion she suffered a serious prolapse and sadly had to be put down. I had to bottle feed her lamb, Topnotch (top right) – he was so cute when he was little, and travelled with me in my Land Rover when I distributed my cards around Dartmoor. Now he is huge, but he still bleats at me, and loves a good rub over his back and on his cheeks!

Baa baa black sheep have you any wool? - Nursery rhyme

Topnotch and friends!

These Dartmoor Whiteface, also known as the Widecombe Whiteface, are descended from the hardy native sheep, which grazed on Dartmoor in their thousands in the 17th and 18th centuries.

Sheepish!

Start

A scrawny old Shetland ewe first appeared in the field with my friend's sheep – no one in the neighbourhood seemed to know anything about her. Then one day, she suddenly had a tiny black lamb beside her. After watching it trying to suck, I noticed that it was getting weaker – if I didn't intervene, I knew the lamb would die. Even so, it was still nimble and wild, and I had to dive for it like a rugby touchdown!

I kept the lamb in a box in my friend's kitchen where I was lodging. For such a tiny creature, she had a big voice which echoed around the house! I called her Start, because I was making a new start after splitting up with my boyfriend, and she followed me everywhere.

She was a hoggett (a one year old) when I went to check on her in the pouring rain, while she was grazing with the other sheep. She heard my voice and staggered towards me, calling urgently. I got her into shelter but she died later that evening. I could only think that as an orphan lamb, she hadn't got the all-important 'collostrum' from her mother, which is produced during the first hours after being born, and fortifies their immune system for life. I was so sad to lose my little Start.

Zeeba

Widecombe Whiteface also know as Dartmoor Whiteface

Poll Dorset

The Lord is my shepherd; I shall not want.
He makes me lie down in green pastures; He leads me beside still waters,
He restores my soul. - Psalm 23

The Cotswold, a descendent of a breed from Roman times, was crossed with the Dartmoor. This produced the Dartmoor Greyface, with longer wool. They grazed the fringes of the moor, while the more agile Whitefaced Dartmoors lived on the high ground.

Badger face Welsh Mountain

A molehill for a pillow! Exmoor Horn lambs.

The Exmoor Horn's fleece is softer 'handling' than most hill breeds – a word used to describe how the wool feels, ranging from soft to harsh. The 'wool staple' describes the pattern of the wool wave, and the 'staple length' is the average length of the hairs. They are measured in microns (a millionth of a metre).

Left: Welsh Mountain, a very hardy sheep, originated from Wales.

Devon and Cornwall Longwool were developed from two old West Country breeds, the South Devon and Devon Longwool, and have a massive heavy fleece with open lustrous curls. This wool is mostly used for carpets.

Devon & Cornwall Longwool

Devon and Cornwall Longwool

Dartmoor Whiteface

Widecombe-in-the-Moor

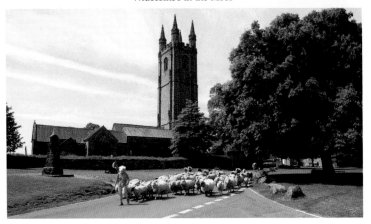

My sheep hear My voice, and I know them, and they follow me. - Gospel of St. John

The wool industry prospered on Dartmoor. The handsome Widecombe Church tower was built at the end of the 15th and early 16th century and paid for by the profits earned by the wool trade and tin mining. When the mining declined, along with the population, the wool trade continued to flourish. In 1850, Widecombe's annual fair, famous for its folk song 'Old Uncle Tom Cobley', was started for sheep, ponies and cattle. The sheep were drifted off the moor, penned by the church yard wall and offered for "sale by the yard!"

A Jacob ewe with her newborn twins, one of which grew into a big ram!

Jacob sheep are believed to be recorded in Genesis, in the Bible, when Jacob produced "spotted and speckled sheep". They were introduced to Britain in the 17th century, as a fashionable parkland breed.

And it happened, at the time when the flocks conceived, that I lifted my eyes and saw in a dream, and behold, the rams which leaped upon the flocks were streaked, speckled and grey-spotted.

Genesis 31

Above: Greyface Dartmoor, Jacob, Ryeland

Above: Exmoor Horn

Above: Blue Texel. Below: Blackface

Above: Devon Closewool & Texel. Below: British Charolla

bove: Suffolks. Below Manx Loaghtan

Above: Wensleydale

Below: North Country Cheviot & Devon Closewool

Above: Exmoor Horn & Jacob. Below: Texel

I may not be totally perfect but parts of me are excellent!
- Ashleigh Brilliant

Wensleydales, with outstanding crimped and curly, lustrous wool. Right: Ryeland, which was developed by the monks of Leominster, Herefordshire, over 800 years ago.

Champion D & C Longwool

Above: Devon & Cornwall Longwool

Above: Hampshire Down

Above: Exmoor Horn. Below: Dartmoor Greyface.   Above: Devon Closewool

Above: Ryeland. Below: Zwartbles

ing the British Charollais & Hampshire Down

Texel

North Country Cheviot

ove: Vendeen. Below: Teeswater

Above: Judging. Below: Champion Charollais and Texel.

Above : Border Leicester

The ancient Dartmoor longhouse was used to house both people and animals. They used the same entrance, with people on one side and livestock on the other.

My uncle Edwin Pearse, blade-sheared 60 longwool sheep a day.
He slept on the wool bales to go on the next day. - Colin Pearse

Sheep are shorn every summer and their wool fleeces are scoured (washed) and carded (fibres combed into one direction). This is done at a grading depot, or by hand by people who use the wool to hand spin, weave or dye. All the wool is tested to measure the micron (thickness of the fibre) and the colour, and is sold to buyers around the world through computer-based auctions.

Above: A beautiful, lustrous Whitefaced fleece

Whether it's the products you use to furnish your home or the clothes you choose to wear, it's clear nature has the edge on the man-made competition.

- HRH Price Charles,
patron of Campaign for Wool

Wool is an incredible natural fibre. The 'out-in-all-weather' sheep grow a new fleece every year, making it a valuable natural resource, and providing man with one of the most effective, natural forms of all-weather protection. It is breathable and can absorb moisture or sweat from the skin. It also reacts to changes in your body to keep you warm when it's cold, or releases heat when it's hot. Wool is not only suited to clothing: it is also ideal for carpets and bedding, as it doesn't easily catch fire and it helps to prevent allergies because it resists dust mites.

Wool has enjoyed a major resurgence recently, with many top fashion retail outlets recognising its unique properties. As one advertising campaign states: "Live naturally and choose wool: It's warm, safe and gentle on the planet."

Above: This young ram has a 'guinea spot' on his nose and the lamb has one on the back of her neck. This was called a purity factor. It appears as a black spot on the Whitefaced Dartmoor sheep, and was worth a guinea (21 shillings, or £1.05) – in fact, rams are still sold in guineas at sales today.

Season of mists and mellow fruitfulness
- John Keats

A laid-back attitude lengthens ones life! Proverb

Do they really want us to go this fast?!

Suffolk

If you don't blend in - you may as well stand out!

The late summer Chagford sheep sales are a traditional event, linked to the 'drifting' of sheep off the moor and its fringes. The farmers would sell breeding sheep and consignments of wether (castrated male) lambs, who would then feed on root crops or grass in the lower country.

Kerry Hill

Hampshire Down

Bluefaced Leicester sheep at Okehampton show. These sheep evolved over a century ago in Northumberland, specifically for breeding high quality, cross-bred ewes from the hardy hill varieties. It is one of the UK's tallest sheep, and produces a soft wool.

SHEEP AROUND THE WORLD!

ITALY ~ GREECE

The sound of bells echoing across the valleys and mountain tops made me feel nostalgic, as I travelled through Europe with my two Greek horses. They would prick their ears forwards, listening to the cheerful notes from the bells, worn by sheep. Simply by listening to this tinkling melody, you could tell when they had their heads down and were calmly nibbling the grass, or were moving at a trot..

Left: An inquisitive sheep which introduced itself while I crossed the mountains in northern Italy.
Above: A Greek shepherd and his small flock outside the village of Agia Efthymia in southern Greece.

FRANCE

Aubrac region, South West France

THE PYRENEES

I encountered these sheep in the Pyrenees, while riding with two Greek horses across Southern Europe.

Prayer walking in Lhasa, Tibet. Buddhists believe in reincarnation, so animals could be their reincarnated relatives.

TIBET

Tibet is called the rooftop of the world, with vast expanses at 16,000ft (5,000m) above sea level, and is home to many sheep, yaks and small ponies. Although yaks are especially common, sheep are also important economically as they provide wool, meat and hides. In many areas, they are also milked, tied together in lines, facing each other. As I travelled through the barren landscape, I saw many flocks and their shepherds, including a boy who looked only about five. He gave me some very solid cheese, the size of dice, on a string.

These sheep are carrying small packs.
Over page: The Himalaya range

Shepherdess with her flock in western Tibet.

COLORADO

Cam the Ramboulet ram parading as the
mascot for the Colorado State University on St.
Patrick's Day in Fort Collins.

NEW MEXICO

Mary had a little lamb. Its fleece was white
as snow and everywhere that Mary went the
lamb was sure to go ....
Nursery rhyme

Monument Valley

The Ramboulet originated when the king of Spain gave some Merino sheep to the king of France in the 14th & 15th century and he created his own breed. Pyrenees dogs run with many flocks in the west of North America as they are exceptional guard dogs and fend off the coyotes, mountain lions and bobcats.

Male sheep use their horns for battering other rams. I met this Rocky Mountain Bighorn ram in Western Canada, on my overland journey to Alaska, after riding horses from Mexico to Canada.

NEW ZEALAND

Above: East Coast, New Zealand.

New Zealand is home to almost four and a half million people, but many more sheep, whose population peaked at over 70 million in the 1980's. In recent years, the sheep population has halved due to the depressed world wool prices, the droughts and competition from other intensive farming activities such as dairy and forestry. British immigrants brought almost every British sheep breed with them to New Zealand. The Perendale is a cross of a Cheviot ram and a Romney ewe, as on Waitomo Farm, Hawkes Bay, in the North Island.

Shearing takes place once a year. A team of shearers and rousies (who sort the wool and pen the sheep) work together as a gang. A 'gun shearer' can remove more than 200 fleeces a day, and can do so without marking or cutting the sheep. Each one takes between two and three minutes, depending on the size and condition of the animal.

Perendale sheep at Waitomo Farm in Hawkes Bay, North Island, New Zealand.

The Merino lamb sales at Tekapo, South Island, New Zealand. Right: Merino rams. The first Merinos were brought to New Zealand by Captain Cook in 1773. Merinos are a specialist breed, producing fine wool which is famous for its use in high quality men's suits, fashion wear and outdoor clothing. As a breed, they thrive in the dry South Island High Country, where they aren't prone to the wool faults, footrot and internal parasites of wetter climates.

Whiteface Dartmoor, Tunhill Fa

Snow dusted Poll Dorset

Blackface gathering snowballs!

In the early 1800s, a large number of Scotch Blackface sheep were imported to Dartmoor by rail, and by ship to Plymouth.

Acknowledgments

British Sheep & Wool. A guide to British Sheep
British Wool Marketing Board

Know Your Sheep Jack Byard

Dartmoor National Park Authority-
Widecombe-in-the-Moor Conservation Area

Rare Breeds Society Trust Fact Sheets

With thanks to:
God, my help and strength
Jonathan Constant for editing
Marian Constant for proofing & ideas
John Mousley for the use of his studio
To all those whose sheep I used as models
Colin, Hazel & Paul Pearse, Barramoor Farm
Simon and Annabel Booty, Sheriel Farm
Rachel and Heather, The Old Rectory
The McCormicks, Waitomo Farm
Simon & Val Tame, Ley Farm
Audrey Stock, Tunhill Farm
Tissa and Nigel Haley
Norma Lamb
Shan Palmes

A Sheepish Farewell!